The Rugrats Movie Storybook

Based on the TV series *Rugrats* created by Klasky/Csupo Inc. and Paul Germain as seen on BBC TV

An imprint of Simon & Schuster UK Ltd
Africa House, 64-78 Kingsway, London WC2B 6AH

POCKET BOOKS and colophon are registered trademarks of Simon & Schuster.
A CIP catalogue for this book is availble from the British Library
ISBN 0-671-02864-2

First Edition   10 9 8 7 6 5 4 3 2 1
Manufactured in the United States of America

The Rugrats Movie Storybook

by Sarah Willson

illustrated by John Kurtz and Sandrina Kurtz

POCKET BOOKS

The Pickleses were having a baby shower. Lots of people were milling around their back garden.

"Any day now, Didi," said Betty.

Didi was staring at the shower gift from her parents. "A goat?" she said to Boris and Minka. "You shouldn't have!"

"Nothing better for the little bubbala than goat's milk," said Grandma Minka.

"Isn't it exciting! They're giving my new baby sister this party because she's gonna be here soon!" said Tommy.

"I wouldn't be in such a hurry if I were you," warned Angelica as she staggered into Tommy's room carrying a huge pile of sweets from the party. "As soon as that baby's born, she's gonna get all your parents' love and attention. They'll forget about you."

"My mummy and daddy won't forget me," said Tommy. But Angelica ignored him and barged out of the room.

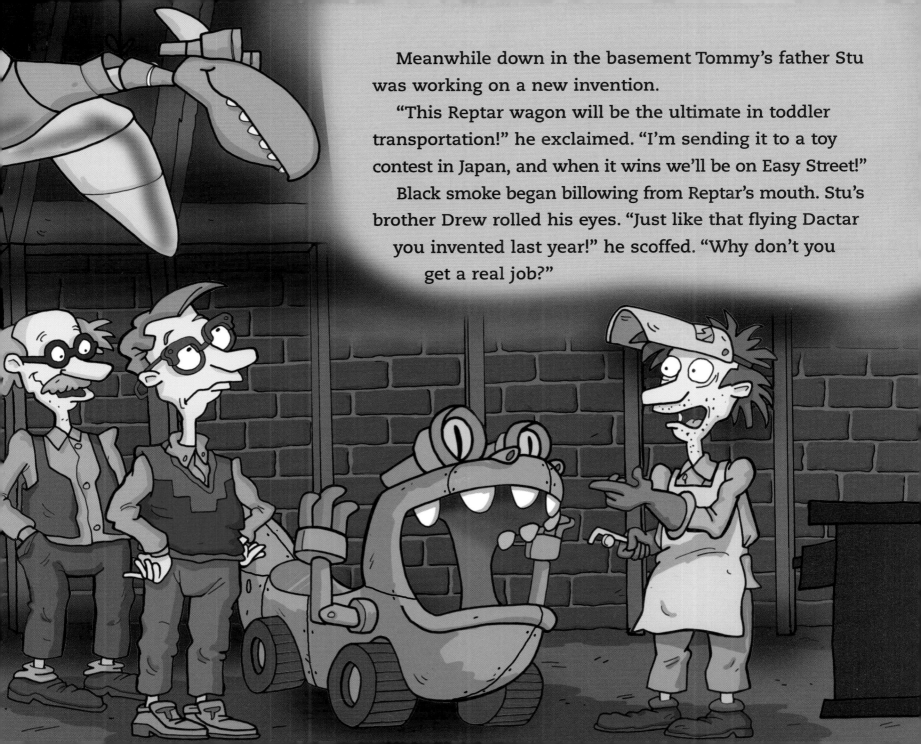

Meanwhile down in the basement Tommy's father Stu was working on a new invention.

"This Reptar wagon will be the ultimate in toddler transportation!" he exclaimed. "I'm sending it to a toy contest in Japan, and when it wins we'll be on Easy Street!"

Black smoke began billowing from Reptar's mouth. Stu's brother Drew rolled his eyes. "Just like that flying Dactar you invented last year!" he scoffed. "Why don't you get a real job?"

Didi was rushed from the party, and later that day she had the baby at the Lipschitz Hospital.

"Oh, Deed!" breathed Stu, looking at the new baby. "She's so beautiful! She's so precious! She's . . . she's a boy!"

They named Tommy's new brother Dylan. "Dil for short. Dil Pickles," said Stu. "I like it."

Tommy was brought into the hospital room to meet Dil.

He reached out to touch his brand-new brother for the first time.

"See," whispered Didi to Betty, "they already love each other."

Tommy soon discovered that life with Dil would be very different. Dil took Tommy's favourite toys and cried a lot, so Tommy didn't get to see his parents very often.

A few weeks after Dil's arrival, Stu took Tommy aside. "I know it's hard having a little brother, Tommy. It's a big responsibility. I want you to have this. It's been in the family a long time."

He handed Tommy a watch, then hugged him.

"Sponsitility," mumbled Tommy to himself, looking at the watch.

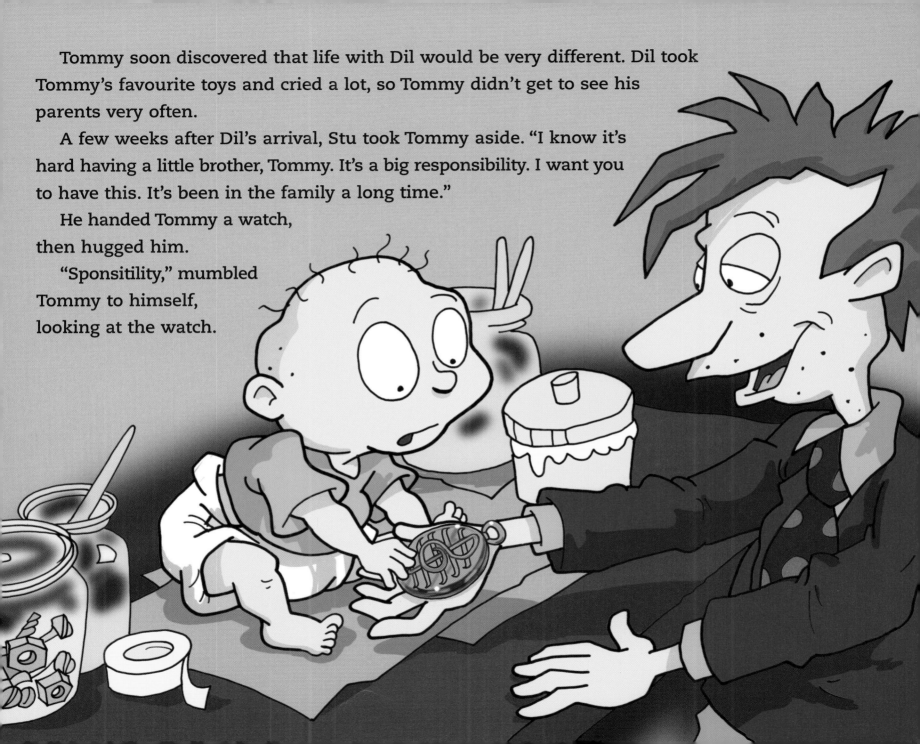

Meanwhile in the living room Grandpa Lou was listening to a television news report about a missing circus train.

Suddenly Grandpa Lou noticed the babies were playing near the Reptar wagon and its shipping crate. "This is no place for you sprouts to be playing! You wouldn't want to get shipped to Japan with Reptar," he added as he carried the crate onto the porch.

"What is it?" asked Chuckie, pointing to the wagon.

"It's Reptar on wheels!" said Lil.

"I bet we could put Dil in it and send him back where he came from," said Phil. "You watch. Once Dil goes away, Tommy will be happy again."

They dumped Dil into the wagon and tossed the changing bag after him.

"Stop! You can't do that!" cried Tommy, hurrying into the room. "My mummy and daddy want to keep him!"

"Why? All he does is cry and poop and take people's toys," said Phil.

Angelica entered the room with her Cynthia doll and Dil grabbed it from her arms.

"You want a ride in a wagon?" Angelica shouted angrily at Dil. "I'll give you a ride . . . to outer space!" And with that she kicked the wagon and left the room.

The wagon began to slowly roll out the front door, gradually picking up speed. "Catch it!" cried Tommy. The babies quickly jumped aboard.

After the babies rolled off, a delivery man came and picked up the empty crate.

Stu woke Grandpa Lou. "Uh, dad, where are the kids? Where is the Reptar crate?" They looked at the spot where the crate had been and saw a baby bottle. A look of horror crossed their faces.

"They've been shipped to Japan!" cried Stu.

As the wagon teetered along, Tommy and Phil fought for control of the steering wheel. The wagon crashed through a lemonade stand, whooshed through a playground, and tore through a mattress factory.

"Aw, Tommy!" cried Chuckie as the wagon bumped along. "Dil just threw up on me!"

The wagon bounced right into the back of a mattress delivery van.

"Uh-oh," said Chuckie as the truck started moving forward.

Stu and Lou zoomed to the airport to try to catch up with the crate. Along the way Stu swerved around the mattress van, forcing it off the road. The driver jumped to safety, and inside the truck the babies giggled as they bounced up and down on piles of mattresses.

When the van stopped, the babies got out and looked around. "Where are we?" wailed Chuckie. "How'll we get back home?"

"Well, I've got my sponsitility," said Tommy. He took it out of his nappy.

"What's a sponsitility, Tommy?" asked Lil.

"It's what you get for bein' a big brother," said Tommy.

"It looks like a crumpus," said Phil.

"Well, my dad gave it to me and he called it a sponsitility," said Tommy. He opened the cover and noticed both hands were pointing to the twelve.

"Let's go straight ahead. Maybe we can find the Lizard. My mum read me a story about him last night. He has a pointy hat and he grants wishes. All we gotta do is say we wanna go home, and everything will be back to Norman."

Back at the Pickles's house, everyone was in a panic.

"Where are my babies?" wailed Didi.

Betty busily passed out fliers.
Stu hatched a plan. "Trust me, Deed," he said. "I'll find 'em." And he ran down to the basement.

Angelica was furious. "Cynthia is missing! That dumb Dil must have taken her! Come on, Spike, let's go find them!" She untied Spike and they ran out into the backyard.

The babies climbed back into the wagon. They rode down the hill and landed in a stream.

"Aaaaaaaah!" they cried. The wagon began to float.

The babies were cranky and started arguing with each other. Lil pulled a packet of sweets from Phil's nappy. Dil threw the sweets, and when Chuckie reached for one he started falling overboard. Then Dil also began tumbling into the water.

"Help me, Tommy!" Chuckie cried out.

Tommy grabbed Dil. Chuckie fell in the water.

"How come you saved him and not me?" Chuckie asked angrily after Phil and Lil had pulled him out.

"I'm sorry, Chuckie, but Dil needed me!" said Tommy.

Clunk! The Reptar boat ran aground.

"Don't worry," said Tommy, "my sponsitility will show us the way to the Lizard."

"I think your sponsitility is broke—just like your brother!" said Lil.

"Yeah, Dil's been causing trouble all day!" said Phil crossly.

"Hey, guys," Chuckie suddenly cried out. "C-c-c-clowns!" He pointed to the wreckage of the missing circus train.

Suddenly the babies were surrounded by monkeys. One of them grabbed Dil's changing bag and ran away. Tommy quickly followed, yelling to his friends, "Watch my brother! I'm going after that bag!"

But while Tommy was away, more monkeys arrived, and one of them snatched up Dil.

Chuckie cried out, "Hey! Leave him alone!" He grabbed Dil and shooed the monkey away.

More monkeys appeared and began pulling on Chuckie and Dil.

Chuckie called, "Hey, guys, help! These monkeys are trying to take Dil!"

"So?" Phil responded.

"Just help me, okay?" cried Chuckie.

Phil and Lil tried to help, but there were too many monkeys. They let go of Dil, and the monkeys carried him off.

When Tommy returned he found Dil was gone. "You told me you would watch him!" he said.

"Look, Tommy, nobody likes Dil," said Lil.

"Yeah, since he came, we never have any fun," added Phil.

"But he's my brother—we have to find him!" said Tommy.

"No, we gotta find that Lizard, Tommy. You can find your brother by yourself," said Phil.

"Come on, Chuckie," pleaded Tommy. "Help me. You're my bestest friend."

"If I'm your bestest friend, how come you didn't help me when I fell overboard?" asked Chuckie. "I'm not coming."

So Tommy went all alone to find Dil. The others went to search for the Lizard. It had started to rain.

Tommy followed the sound of his brother's crying. When he caught up with Dil, he found him being carried away by two monkeys.

"Shoo! Get out of here, you monkeys!" he yelled. "Gimme back my brother!"

Startled, the monkeys let go of Dil.

"C'mon. Let's get out of this rain," Tommy said to Dil as he carried him to a hollow tree. He took out a bottle of milk and a blanket. "Mine!" yelled Dil, grabbing both.

"Phil and Lil were right!" Tommy said angrily. "You're a naughty, bad baby! I'm through being your big brother!" Lightning flashed and thunder boomed. Trembling, Dil latched onto Tommy. Tommy hugged him tight.

"I'm sorry, Dil," said Tommy. "Everything's going to be okay." Dil looked up at Tommy and he gently touched his cheek. Dil's head then slowly dropped onto Tommy's chest and he fell asleep. Tommy smiled down at his sleeping brother.

Suddenly the monkeys returned. The brothers were about to be carried away, when a voice rang out. "Not so fast, monkeys!"

"Phil! Lil!" cried Tommy. "You came back! But where's . . ."

"You want nanners, monkeys? Well, come and get 'em!"

"Chuckie!" cried Tommy.

Chuckie held up an open bottle of banana baby food and ran away, with the monkeys in hot pursuit.

"You guys take Dil and go find the Lizard," shouted Tommy to Phil and Lil. "I gotta go help my bestest friend!"

Angelica and Spike reached the woods. "Dumb dog," said Angelica. "There are no babies here." Spike sniffed the ground and ran off.

At that moment Chuckie burst into the clearing, with the monkeys close behind. "Run, Angelica! The monkeys are coming!"

Angelica noticed that one of the monkeys was holding her Cynthia doll.

"Cynthiaaaaaa!" cried Angelica.

Just as the monkeys closed in on Chuckie, Tommy and Spike crashed into the clearing. Tommy grabbed Chuckie's hand and swept him onto Spike's back. "C'mon, Chuckie! We got a Lizard to see!"

All the babies ran for the Reptar wagon and jumped in. The monkeys were right behind them.

The wagon dropped onto a bridge. "Look! We've found the Lizard's house!" shouted Chuckie, pointing to a ranger station.

Suddenly they heard a menacing growl. The monkeys scampered away. A big, scary wolf blocked their path.

"Spike!" shouted Tommy. They watched as Spike jumped out of the wagon and wrestled with the wolf. Then the two animals plunged off the bridge.

Just then, Stu flew into view. He was flying in his Dactar contraption. "Deed! I found the kids! They're over by the ranger station," he yelled into his radio.

Suddenly Stu crashed through the roof of a nearby shed. He stumbled out in a daze.

"The Lizard!" cried the babies.

"Please, Mr. Lizard," said Tommy, "please grant us one wish. We want our doggie back."

Like magic, Stu's battered radio erupted in sparks, and smoke poured from his helmet.

Then a gust of wind blew Stu into a ravine, where he disappeared.

"See?" said Tommy. "The Lizard went to get Spike. Told you he granted wishes."

A car skidded to a stop, and the babies' parents jumped out. As they ran up, Stu appeared, carrying Spike.

The babies cheered happily.

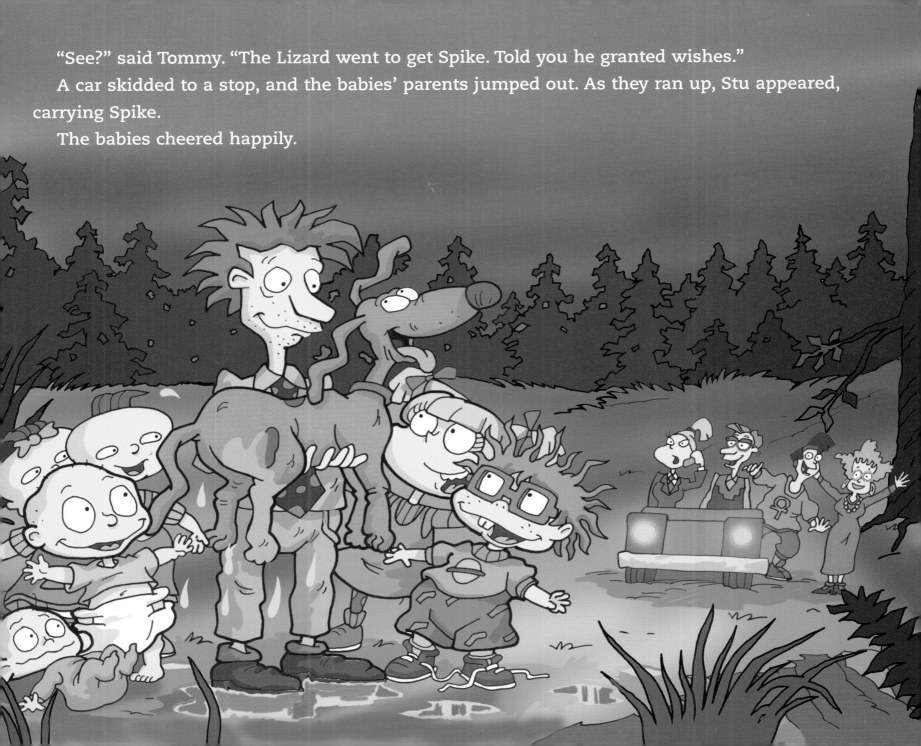

Everyone was brought home safe and sound.

Stu's Reptar wagon won the toy competition.

And if it hadn't been for Tommy's new brother, the babies wouldn't have had such an exciting adventure.

Little Bible Heroes
Christmas

Written by Victoria Kovacs
Illustrated by Mike Krome

B&H
KIDS
NASHVILLE, TENNESSEE

GOLDQUILL
WWW.GOLDQUILL.CO.UK

Published by B&H Publishing Group 2015. Text and illustrations copyright © 2014, GoldQuill, United Kingdom.
All rights reserved. Scripture quotations are taken from the Holman Christian Standard Bible ® Copyright © 1999, 2000, 2002, 2003, 2009 by Holman Bible Publishers. Used by permission. Printed in Heshan, Guangdong, China, May 2019.
ISBN: 978-1-4336-8711-2   Dewey Decimal Classification: CE
Subject Heading: JESUS CHRIST--NATIVITY \ JESUS CHRIST--PASSION WEEK \ BIBLE STORIES
4 5 6 7 8 9 • 23 22 21 20 19

The angel Gabriel appears to Mary. "You will have a Son, and you will name Him Jesus."

Mary visits her old cousin, Elizabeth. Elizabeth is going to have a baby too. Mary tells her, "The Mighty One has done great things for me!"

Mary and Joseph must travel
far away to Bethlehem.

There is no room for them at the inn, so Mary and Joseph go to a place where animals are kept. There Mary gives birth to Jesus on Christmas Day.

Shepherds see angels in the sky saying, "Glory to God!" An angel tells the shepherds that Jesus is born and lying in a manger.

The shepherds hurry to see Jesus.
They know Jesus is a special baby.

The wise men come from the east to worship Jesus. They give Him gold, frankincense, and myrrh.

Read:
Today a Savior, who is Messiah the Lord, was born for you in the city of David.
—Luke 2:11

Think:
1. Why is Christmas special?
2. What gifts can *you* give to Jesus?

Remember:
Thanks be to God for His indescribable gift.
—2 Corinthians 9:15

Read:

"He is not here! For He has been resurrected, just as He said. Come and see the place where He lay."—Matthew 28:6

Think:

1. The day Jesus was resurrected is also called Easter. How do you celebrate Easter?
2. Why is Easter special?

Remember:

"For God loved the world in this way: He gave His One and Only Son, so that everyone who believes in Him will not perish but have eternal life."
—John 3:16

Jesus appears to His disciples.
He is risen!

Mary is so happy that Jesus is alive.

Mary goes back to the tomb, crying.
She hears someone say her name.
She sees Jesus!

Mary tells Jesus' disciples about the empty tomb, but they don't believe her.

Three days later, Mary returns
to the tomb, but it is empty.
She sees an angel. He says,
"Jesus is not here. He is risen!"

After Jesus is placed in a tomb,
Mary goes home to prepare spices
for His burial.

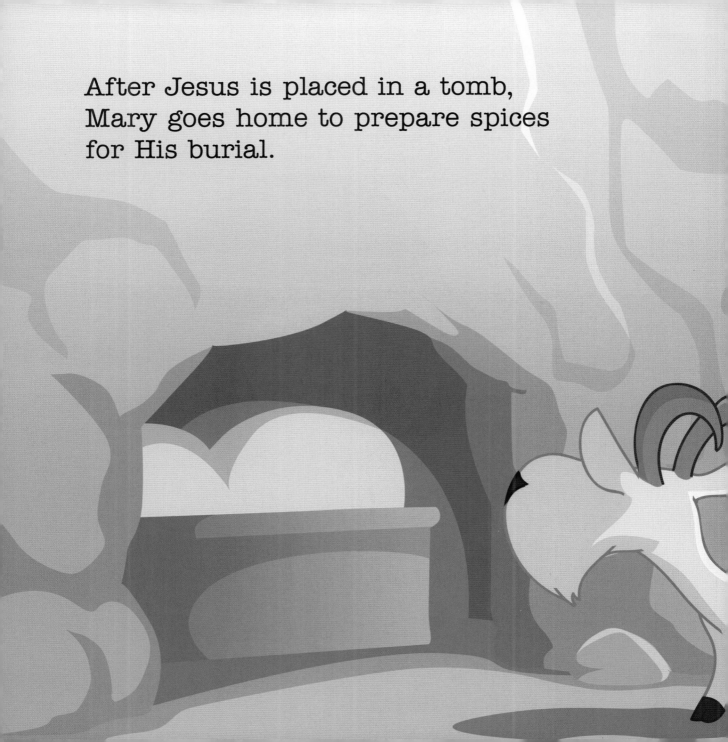

Mary Magdalene is a follower
of Jesus. She is very sad when
Jesus dies on the cross.

Little Bible Heroes™
Easter

Written by Victoria Kovacs
Illustrated by Mike Krome

B&H KIDS

NASHVILLE, TENNESSEE

GOLDQUILL
WWW.GOLDQUILL.CO.UK

Published by B&H Publishing Group 2015. Text and illustrations copyright © 2014, GoldQuill, United Kingdom.
All rights reserved. Scripture quotations are taken from the Holman Christian Standard Bible ® Copyright © 1999, 2000, 2002, 2003, 2009 by Holman Bible Publishers. Used by permission. Printed in Heshan, Guangdong, China, May 2019.
ISBN: 978-1-4336-8711-2   Dewey Decimal Classification: CE
Subject Heading: JESUS CHRIST--NATIVITY \ JESUS CHRIST--PASSION WEEK \ BIBLE STORIES
4 5 6 7 8 9 • 23 22 21 20 19